The Power of CLNC® Focus

Advanced CLNC® Practice-Building Program

The Power of CLNC® Focus

Vickie L. Milazzo, RN, MSN, JD

Vickie Milazzo Institute
National Alliance of Certified Legal Nurse Consultants

5615 Kirby Drive, Suite 425 • Houston, TX 77005-2448
Phone 800.880.0944 • Fax 713.942.8075
LegalNurse.com • mail@LegalNurse.com

Vickie Milazzo Institute
National Alliance of Certified Legal Nurse Consultants

5615 Kirby Drive, Suite 425 • Houston, Texas 77005-2448 • Toll-Free: 800.880.0944
In Houston: 713.942.2200 • Fax: 713.942.8075 • LegalNurse.com • mail@LegalNurse.com

Vickie L. Milazzo, RN, MSN, JD
    President

Dear Colleague:

Welcome to *The Power of CLNC® Focus* from the **Advanced CLNC® Practice-Building Program**. These powerful programs will help you master the skills needed to become an even more **successful Certified Legal Nurse Consultant**CM. By listening to this advanced collection you will:

1. Expand your know-how on a wide range of marketing, consulting and practice management topics essential to your CLNC® success.

2. Learn practical, forward-thinking strategies from nationally known CLNC® Pros.

3. Learn hundreds of CLNC® practice-building tips you can use right away in your legal nurse consulting career.

> If you are a Certified Legal Nurse ConsultantCM, listening to these CDs is the first easy step to extending your CLNC® Certification for one year beyond your current certification expiration date. **You must complete the post test and evaluation form online at LegalNurse.com/AdvPractice and click Submit to qualify for recertification.** Upon successful completion of the test, your CLNC® Certification will be extended one year and you may print your CE certificate.

Congratulations on your journey to CLNC® success as you apply the power of focus. I look forward to hearing your CLNC® success story soon.

Success Is Yours!

Vickie L. Milazzo, RN, MSN, JD

P.S. To check your CLNC® Certification expiration date, view your listing at *NACLNC*directory.org.

About Vickie Milazzo Institute and the Pioneer of Legal Nurse Consulting

Vickie L. Milazzo, RN, MSN, JD

Featured and Published in

- ► *The New York Times*
- ► *USA Today*
- ► *Ladies' Home Journal*™
- ► *Lawyers Weekly USA*
- ► *Entrepreneur*
- ► *MSNBC.com*

Awards

- ► *Inc.* Top Ten Entrepreneur – one of the top 10 entrepreneurs in the U.S.
- ► Stevie Award for Women Entrepreneurs – Mentor of the Year
- ► Most Innovative Small Business by Pitney Bowes
- ► Top 100 Small Businesses in Houston
- ► Top 25 Woman-Owned Businesses in Houston
- ► *NurseWeek* Nursing Excellence Award for Advancing the Profession

Founder and president of Vickie Milazzo Institute, Vickie L. Milazzo, RN, MSN, JD pioneered the field of legal nurse consulting in 1982. *The New York Times* credited her with creating this profession.

The Institute is the nation's oldest and largest legal nurse consulting training institute and the only publishing company devoted exclusively to this field. Vickie created the CLNC® Certification, the first national legal nurse consulting certification, in 1994.

The authoritative educator in this field, Vickie has been profiled in *The New York Times, St. Louis Post-Dispatch, Houston Business Journal, Houston Woman Magazine, JAVA, The Progressive* and *NurseWeek*. Articles featuring Vickie have also been published in *Entrepreneur, Ladies' Home Journal*™, *Houston Chronicle, Pittsburgh Business Times, Small Business Success* and *Lawyers Weekly USA* as well as in more than 220 newspapers reaching 16.6 million readers.

Vickie has been interviewed on TV as an entrepreneur expert and her radio appearances have reached more than 20 million listeners. Her essay, *Stepping Out of Fear*, aired on NPR's *All Things Considered* segment, *This I Believe®*. NPR has an audience of 26 million people.

In addition to editing the bimonthly electronic newsletter, *Legal Nurse Consulting Ezine*, Vickie is the author of the *Core Curriculum for Legal Nurse Consulting®* and

numerous legal nurse consulting textbooks, DVDs and audio CDs.

Her work has been published in many nursing, legal and business publications including *USA Today, Nursing Spectrum, NurseWeek, National Medical-Legal Reporter, Forensic Nurse, JAVA, Association of Trial Lawyers of America Newsletter, American Journal of Nursing* and *Houston Business Journal*.

Vickie received the Stevie Award as Mentor of the Year and the Nursing Excellence Award for Advancing the Nursing Profession. The Institute was recognized as the most innovative small business by Pitney Bowes' *Priority* magazine.

Vickie is the author of the business bestseller, *Inside Every Woman: Using the 10 Strengths You Didn't Know You Had to Get the Career and Life You Want Now*, published by John Wiley & Sons, Inc.

Revolutionizing
Nursing Careers
One RN at a Time Since 1982

Vickie has trained thousands of RNs. She shares not only her own experience, but the experiences of thousands of Certified Legal Nurse Consultants™. She single-handedly created this profession for RNs who are transformed by her extensive business expertise, irresistible drive and vibrant energy.

The Power of CLNC® Focus

CONTENTS

Providing Excellent Customer Service

Evie Baron-Hernandez

PROVIDING EXCELLENT CUSTOMER SERVICE

I.   **THE TWO TYPES OF CUSTOMERS**

    A.   **External Customers**

        1.   Attorney-clients.

        2.   Insurance companies.

        3.   Large corporations.

    B.   **Internal Customers**

        1.   Employees.

        2.   Subcontractors.

        3.   Expert witnesses.

        4.   Vendors.

II. **THE THREE STAGES OF CUSTOMER SERVICE**

    A.   **Pre-Sale Consulting Service**

        1.   Definition – Service provided to a potential client before the deal is closed.

        2.   Time you spend:
            a.   Educating the potential client about your company.
            b.   Training the potential client to use your product or service.
            c.   Promoting your business to make the potential client more aware of your company and how the client company might benefit from your service.

        3.   Pre-sale consulting services are usually the deciding factor for a prospective client to give your company a try.

B. **Transactional Service**

    1.   Definition – Services that enhance a transaction between a firm and its customers.

    2.   Examples:
        a.   Accepting different types of credit cards.
        b.   Being organized when setting up a contact with your client.
        c.   Committing to a delivery date.
        d.   Providing information about guarantees.
        e.   Delivering your products or services efficiently.
        f.   Being accessible to your client when working on a case.
        g.   Providing a wide range of services to your client.
            (1)   Do these services satisfy your client's needs?

    3.   Transactional services make your company easy to do business with.

C. **Post-Sale Services**

    1.   Definition – Services that occur after the transaction.

    2.   "These are the services that have traditionally attracted the most attention by firms."   *– Creating Customer Value*

    3.   Examples:
        a.   Follow-up call to determine customer satisfaction.
        b.   Post-sale support services.
        c.   Post-sale contact.
            (1)   Cards.
            (2)   Letters.
            (3)   Phone calls.
            (4)   Newsletters.

    4.   Post-sale services keep your customer coming back for more because you express a genuine interest in how you can help your client.

III. THE TWO TYPES OF SUPPORT SERVICES

A. Basic Hygiene Support Services

1. Definition – Threshold level of service that customers expect to be there as part of the package.

2. Examples:
   a. Meeting deadlines.
   b. Being on time for meetings.
   c. Acting professionally.

3. Make sure hygiene support services meet the customer's expectations.

4. The absence of hygiene factors will probably result in customer dissatisfaction, but the presence of hygiene factors won't necessarily contribute to customer satisfaction.

B. Support Service Satisfiers

1. Definition – Services that go beyond the level of hygiene services and surpass the customer's more basic expectations.

2. Examples:
   a. Software companies have a 1-800 number to walk customers through steps of using new software instead of reading the manual.
   b. Grocery store customizes the thickness of my lunch meat to my preference.
   c. You can send out comic strips or articles that may be amusing or of interest to your client.

3. Support service satisfiers:
   a. Nurture a strong relationship with your client.
   b. Help increase customer retention.
   c. Set you apart from the others, creating a unique competitive advantage that may result in customer delight.

4. Your customer may be willing to pay more for your products or services because of the added support service.

IV. IMPORTANT CUSTOMER SERVICE SKILLS

A. Reliable

1. Deliver what you promised.

B. Dependable

1. Meet all deadlines.

C. Accurate

1. Make sure all information you give your client is presented accurately.
   a. Your credibility is very hard to reestablish.

D. Responsive

1. Be willing to help promptly.

2. Find out what each client thinks is an appropriate wait for each type of service or response:
   a. Returning phone calls.
   b. Finding an expert witness.
   c. Problem solving.
   d. Researching or finding an answer to a question.

E. Reassuring

1. "Courtesy is not a substitute for good customer service."

2. Your client will be reassured that your service is first-rate if you:
   a. Know your products.
   b. Understand your client's lingo.
   c. Have clinical experience.
   d. Are familiar with your client's company history.
   e. Are familiar with your client's company policies.
   f. Offer assurance that your vendors, employees and subcontractors also know your client's expectations.

F. **Empathy**

    1.   Provide individual attention and show your customers how much you care.

    2.   Recognizing your client's emotional state will help you figure out how to serve her effectively and professionally.
        a.   Empathy helps you stay in control of the situation.
        b.   Sympathy will send you on an emotional roller-coaster ride that can keep you from focusing your attention on what is wrong.

G. **Listening Skills**

    1.   The importance of good listening:
        a.   Helps you figure out what your customer wants and needs.
        b.   Can prevent errors and misunderstandings.
        c.   Gives you clues about how to improve your service.
        d.   Helps build long-term customer relationships.

    2.   Be committed to being a good listener.
        a.   Develop an interest in the conversation and topic.
        b.   Be self-disciplined when expressing ideas, using body language, and eliminating distractions.
        c.   Stay focused on what the client is saying to you.
        d.   People who are good listeners are not born that way. It's never too late to become a good listener.

V. THREE WAYS TO MAKE YOUR CUSTOMERS RIGHT

A. **Assume the Customer Is Innocent**

    1.   If what the customer is saying sounds wrong to you:
        a.   Assume they are explaining poorly what they want or need, or
        b.   Assume they are not aware of important information that might make what they want impossible.

B. **Look for Opportunities to Teach the Customer**

    1.   What information could your customer have used before the misunderstanding occurred? Make sure they get it now.

C. Believe in Your Customer

1. Sometimes the customer you initially think is absolutely wrong turns out to be right.

2. Remember, the customer is not the enemy, and it is important to keep your customer relationship intact.

3. When in doubt, assume your customer is right until you find out otherwise.

VI. DEALING WITH UNHAPPY CUSTOMERS

A. Show Empathy

1. Apologize for the problem and show sincere concern, regardless of whether or not the problem is your fault.

B. Allow Your Customer to Vent

1. Let the customer get the problem off his chest.

C. Listen Actively

1. To understand.

2. To confirm.

D. Fix the Problem Fairly and Quickly

1. The bottom line is the customer expects to receive what he wanted in the first place; therefore, the sooner you correct the problem, the better.

E. Offer Atonement

1. The average customer wants you to offer a value-added gesture that says, "I'm sorry. Maybe this will make it up to you."

F.   **Keep Your Promises**

       1.   When you are in service recovery, make sure you deliver what is promised or the outcome could be devastating to your relationship with that client.

G.   **Follow Up**

       1.   Make sure your customer is satisfied by following up hours, days or weeks later.

VII. CUSTOMER LOYALTY AND RETENTION

A.   **Why Is It Important to Create Loyal Customers?**

       1.   Regular and repeat purchasing.

       2.   Cross-section purchasing.

       3.   Referring other customers.

       4.   Resisting competitors.

B.   **Creating Customer Loyalty**

       1.   Distinguish yourself and your services from the competition in the customer's eyes.

       2.   Benchmark your services.

       3.   Cultivate staff loyalty.

VIII. HOW CAN I PROVIDE MY CLIENTS WITH EXCELLENT CUSTOMER SERVICE?

A.   Make a List of All the Services You Would Like to Offer Your Client

B.   Create a System to Add These Services to Your Practice

C.   Schedule the Date When You Plan to Have Each of These Services in Place

"It is just the little touches after the average man would quit that make the master's fame."
– Orison Swett Marden

	Basic Hygiene Support Services	Support Service Satisfiers
Pre-Sale Consulting Services		
Transactional Services		
Post-Sale Services		

10

How to Enhance Your Practice with Pro Bono Work and Seminars

Tamara Schilling, RN, BSN, CLNC

HOW TO ENHANCE YOUR PRACTICE WITH PRO BONO WORK AND SEMINARS

I. **HOW TO GET THE BUSINESS**

    A.   **Create Your "Widget" and Sell It**

II. **HOW TO PLAN FOR SUCCESS USING A MARKETING PLAN**

    A.   **Company Vision**

    B.   **Goals**

    C.   **Yearly Income**

    D.   **Customers**

          1.   How many? Size of my practice?

          2.   What kind of attorneys?

    E.   **Subcontractors**

          1.   Will I use subcontractors or not?

    F.   **Marketing Budget**

          1.   How much will I set aside for marketing?

          2.   How much time will I devote?
                  a.   Per day, week, month?

3. How will I market my services?
   a. Involvement in local bar association.
   b. Speaking and presenting educational seminars.

III. HOW TO CREATE A DEMAND FOR YOUR SERVICES

A. How Will I Demonstrate My Quality and Professionalism?

1. Quality business cards.

2. Logo.

3. Stationery.

4. Marketing brochure.

5. My personal appearance.

6. My preparedness for meetings.
   a. In person.
   b. Over the telephone.

B. How Will I Demonstrate My Reliability?

1. Return phone calls promptly.

2. Get work product done on schedule.

3. Keep client aware of progress during projects.

4. Keep my promises.

C. Get Exposed!

IV. HOW TO GAIN EXPOSURE BY ESTABLISHING A PRESENCE IN THE LEGAL COMMUNITY

A. Determine Your Interests

    1.   Decide what area of law you are interested in.

    2.   Decide what type of attorney you want to target.

B. Target Appropriate Attorneys

    1.   Contact the local bar association and ask for information on:
        a.   Committees you can join.
        b.   Pro bono opportunities.

C. Offer Pro Bono Services in Your Area of Interest

    1.   Call the pro bono or legal assistance program chairperson and tell them you are not an attorney but a nurse who does medical-legal consulting.

    2.   Offer your assistance in the following areas:
        a.   Child abuse and neglect.
            (1)   Review the medical records.
            (2)   Serve as a volunteer advocate and case manager. (Many advocates for children are volunteer social workers or just about *anyone* who will do the work.)
        b.   Domestic violence.
            (1)   Review the medical records.
            (2)   Serve as a key resource person to help connect victims with community services.
        c.   Elder abuse.
            (1)   Review the medical records (which are key in prosecuting these cases).
            (2)   Educate the volunteer attorneys handling litigation.
        d.   Homeless advocacy.
            (1)   Gather and review medical documentation.
                (a)   List conditions.
                (b)   List medications.

        (2)   Help homeless person file SSI applications. **(Exhibits A-D)**

            (a)   Disability Report (Federal Form SSA-3368-F6).

            (b)   Vocational Report (Federal Form SSA-3369-F6).

            (c)   Daily Activities Questionnaire.

        (3)   Attend the Disability Adult Programs Division (DAPD) Consultative Exam (CE) on behalf of the homeless person. **(Exhibit E)**

            (a)   Same as an Independent Medical Exam (IME).

        (4)   Work with the disability analyst from the government DAPD (and write a persuasive letter).

            (a)   Your RN skills can greatly assist overburdened government disability analysts.

            (b)   Your case evaluation and assessment can move paperwork along quickly, helping the government process valid claims for deserving individuals who may not be able to advocate for themselves.

        (5)   Assist with appeals.

V.   HOW TO USE SPEAKING ENGAGEMENTS TO GAIN EXPOSURE

A.   How to Put Together a Professional Education Class

1.   Choose a topic.

    a.   List 3 topics that you can speak on.

        (1)

        (2)

        (3)

    b.   Keep your topic basic.

        (1)   Trust that the audience really does not know what you do.

        (2)   Do not give away all your goodies for free – teach your audience *why* they need to retain you.

2.   Develop an outline for your topic.

    a.   Decide how long your presentation will be.

        (1)   Keep it to 30 minutes (and never over one hour).

3.   Target attorneys or firms you would like to speak for.

    a.   Start small to get your feet wet – don't go after your dream client right away.

        b.   Call your state bar association.
- (1) Ask for their information packet for prospective Minimum Continuing Legal Education (MCLE) providers. **(Exhibits F-H)**
- (2) Read this information CAREFULLY and abide by all rules and regulations.
  - (a) *e.g.,* the State of California prohibits certain types of advertising when promoting an MCLE course.

4. Approach your target firm.
   - a. Secure a date for your presentation.
   - b. Practice, practice, practice.
     - (1) Practice delivering your speech to anyone who will listen – the bathroom mirror, your best friend, spouse, dog, anyone!
     - (2) Know your presentation well enough to recite it without looking at your notes.
     - (3) Regardless of what you say, your delivery will make a lasting impression on your audience.
     - (4) If you need help with public speaking, join a Toastmasters group (listed in phone directory under Toastmasters).
   - c. Get to know a little about your audience before you speak.
     - (1) Know who will attend.
     - (2) Arrive early and, if possible, introduce yourself to a few participants before you speak.

5. Do it!
   - a. Remember this one thing: People will forgive ANYTHING except being bored! – Speak with enthusiasm!
   - b. Record your presentation on tape.
     - (1) Listen to yourself later to refine your presentation.

6. Ask for the business!
   - a. When you finish speaking, talk to as many participants as you can.
   - b. In one week, follow up with a nice letter to all participants, including your business card, to keep you fresh in their minds.
   - c. If anyone spoke with you about a case, call and ask for the case.
     - (1) Do not wait for them to call you – they are busy, they will forget, but you mustn't!
   - d. Get feedback from your audience and continually seek to improve your talk for your next presentation.

7. Do the next one!
    a. With each talk you give, you get better and they get easier to do.
    b. Shamelessly market your programs.
        (1) Highlight the fact that you offer MCLE accredited classes.
        (2) Name drop where you've spoken before.
        (3) Mention specialized presentations you have given in the past.

Exhibit A

BAYBAC Clients SSI/SSDI Cases
INTAKE SHEET

Advocate_____

Phone (_____)_____Fax (_____)_____

Client Identifier_____
(first 2 initials of first name, first 2 of last name, last 4 digits of Social Security Number)

City _____

County _____

District Office_____

Date of 1ˢᵗ meeting with client_____

Date Claim filed (current application)_____

Re-application b/c of DAA?   ❑ Yes ❑ No

Continuing disability review (CDR)? ❑ Yes ❑ No

Age   _____

Gender   ❑ Male   ❑ Female ❑ Other

Veteran   ❑ Yes   ❑ No

Family status❑ Single(divorced/widowed) ❑ Married/Partner   ❑Children(dependent)

Ethnicity   ❑ White   ❑ Latino   ❑ Asian-Am ❑ African-Am ❑ Native-Am ❑ Other

Disability ❑ Physical   ❑ Mental   ❑ Both

Applied for SSI benefits before? ❑ Yes ❑ No

If yes, got Benefits? ❑ Yes ❑ No

If no, denied at: ❑ initial application ❑ reconsideration ❑ hearing ❑uncertain

Intake Notes:

Exhibit B

BAYBAC Clients SSI/SSDI Cases
CLOSURE SHEET

Advocate _____

Phone _____ Fax_____

Client Identifier _____
    (first 2 initials of first name, first 2 of last name, last 4 digits of Social Security Number.)

County _____ City _____

District Office _____

DED Office _____

Analyst (init. app) _____ Analyst (recon) _____

DHU Officer _____ ALJ _____

Date of:

    init. decision:_____ appeal/DHU Hearing:_____

    recon/DHU hearing decision: _____ appeal: _____

    ALJ hearing:_____ decision: _____

Date case closed _____

Results   ❑ granted   ❑ denied   ❑ lost contact w/ client

If Granted, at what stage:

    ❑ initial application/re-app   ❑ reconsideration/DHU   ❑ ALJ hearing

Disability Information - (check ALL that apply):

❑ **Physical**
    ❑ mobility
    ❑ orthopedic/arthritis (e.g. back, leg, shoulder pain)
    ❑ seizures
    ❑ asthma
    ❑ HIV
    ❑ gastro-intestinal (e.g. pancreaitis, liver/ kidney disfunction)
    ❑ cardio-pulmonary (e.g., stroke, high blood pressure)
    ❑ cancer
    ❑ diabetes
    ❑ blind
    ❑ other (please explain below)

❑ **Mental**
    ❑ organic
    ❑ psychosis
        ❑ schizophrenia
        ❑ paranoia
        ❑ other
    ❑ affective disorders
        ❑ depression
        ❑ bipolar
    ❑ developmental disabilities
        ❑ mental retardation
        ❑ autism
    ❑ anxiety disorders (e.g. PTSD)
    ❑ personality disorders
        ❑ borderline
        ❑ antisocial
        ❑ dependent
    ❑ somataform disorders (e.g., pain or other problem not attributable to physical causes)
    ❑ other (please explain below)

Disability notes:

19

Exhibit C

Barriers Encountered - (*check ALL that apply*):

❏ **Lack of knowledge about benefits**
    ❏ that they are available
    ❏ unclear about eligibility
    ❏ where to go
    ❏ how to apply

❏ **Disability Related**
    ❏ could not understand what to do
    ❏ ashamed to apply
    ❏ could not physically go through
       application procedure

❏ **Difficulty with process**
    ❏ confusion with entire process
    ❏ did not understand forms
    ❏ did not understand communication from SSA
    ❏ no access to legal/good representation (*please explain below*)
    ❏ missed deadlines
    ❏ missed mail
    ❏ difficulty making appointments

❏ **Difficulty documenting disability**
    ❏ missed medical appointments
    ❏ no access to health or mental health treatment
    ❏ inadequate Consultative Exams

❏ **Problems with SSA Staff** (*please note specific problems and explain below*)
    ❏ claims representative
    ❏ DED analyst at initial stage
    ❏ DED analyst at reconsideration
    ❏ DHU hearing officer
    ❏ Administrative Law Judge
    ❏ Consultative Examiner

❏ **Delay**
    ❏ incarcerated
    ❏ lost track of the process
    ❏ moved and did not keep up with process
    ❏ Delay caused by SSA/DED (*please explain below*)

❏ **Other** (*please explain below*)

<u>Comments:</u>

Exhibit D

AUTHORIZATION FOR RELEASE OF INFORMATION

I hereby authorize _____to release to [Your Organization's Name], its attorneys, staff, and advocates, any and all information in your possession, including sensitive information regarding my physical and mental condition, drug and/or alcohol use, jail/prison/parole, employment, military, and or educational history.

TYPE OF INFORMATION:

I understand that this information will be used only for the purpose of helping document my Social Security Disability/SSI claim. This authorization will remain in effect until revoked by me in writing. Photocopies of this authorization will be as valid as the original.

Full Name:

Social Security Number:

Date of Birth: _____ CDC#:

Address:

Signature:

Date:

Exhibit E

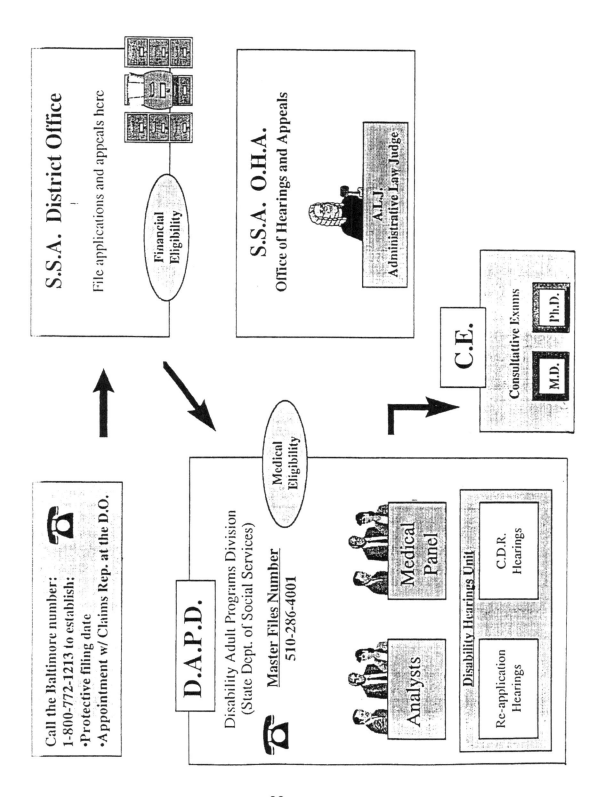

Exhibit F

OFFICIAL RECORD OF ATTENDANCE FOR CALIFORNIA MCLE

Provider: _____

Subject Matter/Title: _____

Date and Time of Activity: _____

Location: _____

Length of Activity: _____

ELIGIBLE CALIFORNIA MCLE CREDIT:

TOTAL HOURS: [_____]

Legal Ethics: _____

Law Practice Management: _____

Civil and Criminal Remedies Available for Civil Rights Violations: _____

Elimination of Bias in the Legal Profession: _____

Prevention, Detection and Treatment of. . .

Substance Abuse: _____

Emotional Distress: _____

Name of Attendee	California State Bar No.	Attendee Signature

REMINDER TO PROVIDER: Keep this record of attendance for 4 years after the date of completion of this activity.

Exhibit G

ACTIVITY EVALUATION FORM FOR CALIFORNIA MCLE

Please complete and return to Provider   Please Print

Provider Name   _____

Provider Phone #   _____

Provider Address   _____

Title of Activity   _____

Date of Offering   _____   Site _____

Name of Participant _____   _____
(optional)   First   Last

_____

Directions: On a scale of 1-5 (5 being the highest, best or most and 1 being the least, lowest or worst) rate by circling the number reflecting your opinion.

To what extent were your personal objectives satisfied?

Comments: _____   5 4 3 2 1

To what extent did the environment contribute to the learning experience?

Comments: _____   5 4 3 2 1

To what extent did the written materials contribute to the learning experience?

Comments: _____   5 4 3 2 1

To what extent were the objectives stated in the promotional literature or those stated at the beginning of the activity satisfied?

Comments: _____   5 4 3 2 1

To what extent did the activity contain significant current intellectual or practical content?

Comments: _____   5 4 3 2 1

_____

Please rate the faculty on the same scale.

		Overall Teaching Effectiveness	Effectiveness of Teaching Methods	Significant Current Intellectual or Practical Content
Instructor's Name:	_____	5 4 3 2 1	5 4 3 2 1	5 4 3 2 1
Subject/Topic:	_____			
Comments:	_____			
Instructor's Name:	_____	5 4 3 2 1	5 4 3 2 1	5 4 3 2 1
Subject/Topic:	_____			
Comments:	_____			
Instructor's Name:	_____	5 4 3 2 1	5 4 3 2 1	5 4 3 2 1
Subject/Topic:	_____			
Comments:	_____			

Exhibit H

State Bar of California
Office of Certification
100 Van Ness Avenue, 28th Floor
San Francisco, CA 94102-5238
(415) 241-2100

Activity Approval
Minimum Continuing Legal Education

FOR OFFICE USE ONLY

PROV. #: _____

❑ $75 ❑ No check

APP.#: _____

❑ RETURNED TO COMPLETE

DATE: _____

---

1. NAME OF PROVIDER

2. NAME OF ACTIVITY

   PREVIOUSLY APPROVED? ❑ Yes ❑ No
   (If yes, attach a copy of the original approval letter.)

3. CONTACT PERSON

4. PROVIDER PHONE (Area Code)

   CONTACT PHONE (Area Code)

5. MAILING ADDRESS

6. STREET ADDRESS (If different from mailing address.)

7. TYPE OF PROVIDER (check one)

❑ CA District Atty. Assn.   ❑ CA Public Defender Assn. ❑ Commercial Educator   ❑ Corporate Counsel   ❑ Educational Institution   ❑ Government Agency

❑ Non-Legal Professional Assn.   ❑ Law Firm   ❑ Local Bar Assn.   ❑ Professional Assn.   ❑ Individual   ❑ State Bar

Other (describe): _____

8. NATURE OF ACTIVITY

❑ Live Presentation
❑ Audiovisual
❑ Skills Workshop
❑ Self-Study/Self Assessment Test
❑ Online (describe) _____
❑ Other (describe) _____

9. DATE(S) AND SITE(S) OF PRESENTATION(S)

1st DATE: _____

SITE: _____

2nd DATE: _____

SITE: _____
(Attach a list of additional dates, if applicable.)

❑ Date and/or site to be announced

10. DESCRIBE WRITTEN MATERIALS FOR ATTENDEES

❑ None (Not required if activity is one hour or less.)

❑ State Total Number of Pages: _____ (Required if activity is more than one hour.)

❑ Looseleaf   ❑ Bound   ❑ Other: _____
(Do not submit course materials with this application.)

11. If retroactive approval is sought:

   Number of Attendees: _____

   Percentage of Attorneys in Attendance: _____ %

MCLE—Activity Approval

12. METHODS OF EVALUATION USED (check all that apply; see Rule 7.2.9)

❏ CA MCLE Evaluation Form (Please see Form CE-107.)

❏ Other (Please submit a **SAMPLE** for approval, with this application. Providers shall make available to each participant a copy of the State Bar approved Education Form or other evaluation form soliciting at least the same information.)

13. OUTLINE OF COURSE PRESENTATION. DETAIL THE TIME PERIOD WITHIN WHICH EACH SEGMENT OF THE ACTIVITY OCCURRED, LIST THE SUBJECT AND CALCULATE THE CREDIT IN MINUTES. FOR INSTANCE:

BEGIN	END	SUBJECT	FACULTY/TITLE	CREDIT	SUBFIELD CREDIT
9:00	10:15	Arbitration Training	John Q. Doe, Attorney	75 Minutes	0 Minutes
10:15	10:30	Coffee Break		0 Minutes	0 Minutes
10:30	11:30	Elimination of Bias in the Courtroom	Mary O. Smith, UCLA Law Prof.	60 Minutes	60 Minutes Bias

Total minutes of instruction is divided by 60 to determine the total hours, rounding up or down to the nearest quarter hour; i.e., 135 minutes = 2.25 hours; the Elimination of Bias credit = 60 minutes = 1 hour. California MCLE credit is given for introduction, opening remarks, and question and answer periods. If you indicate that a luncheon speech was given, you must indicate the exact running time of the speech and how it qualifies for legal education. In the last column, indicate if credit was given in any of the following subfields: Legal Ethics; Law Practice Management; Civil and Criminal Remedies for Civil Rights Violations; Prevention, Detection and Treatment of Substance Abuse and Emotional Distress; Elimination of Bias in the Legal Profession. Subfields must be specified in detail, not just listed; e.g., "Rules of Professional Conduct", not just "Ethics". NOTE: The time spent in any lunch, coffee, or stretch breaks should not be included in the total credit hours you calculate.

BEGIN	END	SUBJECT	FACULTY/TITLE	CREDIT	SUBFIELD
Attach additional sheet, if applicable.) INCOMPLETE FORMS WILL BE RETURNED			Total Minutes =		
			Divide By 60 = (Round up/down to nearest 1/4 hr.)		

14. PLEASE PROVIDE A SHORT EXPLANATION OF HOW THIS ACTIVITY RELATES TO LEGAL SUBJECTS AND OTHERWISE COMPLIES WITH SECTION 7.1.

_____

_____

15.   **ATTESTATION**

Provider acknowledges that approval for this activity may be revoked for non-compliance with the MCLE Rules and Regulations, and amendments thereto, or for failure to comply with the agreements and certifications contained in this form.

Provider certifies that this education activity meets the standards specified in Section 7.1 of the MCLE Rules and Regulations.

Provider agrees to comply with all of the requirements specified in Section 7.2 of the MCLE Rules and Regulations.

Provider agrees to comply with all other MCLE Rules and Regulations applicable to providers that are promulgated by the State Bar of California.

If provider uses promotional materials prior to activity approval, provider agrees to specify in all such materials that application for activity approval is pending and to advise all participants as soon as possible whether or not activity approval is granted.

I HAVE READ THE FOREGOING ANSWERS AND STATEMENTS ON THIS FORM AND ON ANY ATTACHMENTS TO IT AND KNOW THE CONTENTS THEREOF, AND THE SAME IS TRUE OF MY OWN KNOWLEDGE. I DECLARE UNDER PENALTY OF PERJURY, UNDER THE LAWS OF THE STATE OF CALIFORNIA, THAT THE FOREGOING AND ANY ATTACHMENTS TO IT ARE TRUE AND CORRECT.

PROVIDER NAME: _____   BY: _____
                                                          (Print Name and Title)

DATE: _____   SIGNATURE: _____

MCLE—Activity Approval

The Power of
Focused Marketing

Vickie L. Milazzo, RN, MSN, JD

THE POWER OF FOCUSED MARKETING

I. FOCUS

A. Focus Is the Theme of This Program

B. What Exactly Is Focus?

1. A center of activity, attraction or attention.

2. Sharp, laser focus is essential for quantum success.

II. THREE ASSUMPTIONS WE WILL MAKE TODAY

A. Overdiversification Can Kill a Business

B. Focus Is Counter-Intuitive

1. Your intuition will discourage you from focusing.
    a. Most entrepreneurs look for ways to expand the services they offer.
    b. Actually, you will grow faster if you specialize.

2. Look around you at all the companies that have their hands in too many things. These companies are failing.
    a. The big mega-conglomerates that do succeed are made up of smaller, highly *focused* divisions.

C. We Must Focus on the Right Questions

1. The answers are only as good as the quality of the questions we ask.
    a. Example – Instead of asking, "*Is the market saturated?*" we should be asking, "*What do I need to do to penetrate the market?*"

III. FOCUS STRATEGIES[1]

A. A Focus Is Simple

1. Your marketing strategies should be focused and simple.

2. Avoid having too many cooks in the kitchen.
   a. The more people who are involved in the vision process, the more likely you will be to lose the laser-sharp focus.
   b. The focus will become blurred.

3. Look to your unique selling position (USP) to help you develop your marketing focus as well as your vision.

B. A Focus Is Memorable

1. Since a focus has to work in the mind of the client, it must be memorable.
   a. A memorable focus is unique.
   b. A memorable focus contains an element of shock.

C. A Focus Is Powerful

1. Focus increases your potential for success and power.

2. Focus should empower you to take action.
   a. Focus should propel you toward your goal.
   b. You want to create a focus so powerful that you can't help but act on it, and your competitors can't help but try to copy you and strive to destroy you.

D. A Focus Is Revolutionary

1. A focus is radical.

---

[1] Based on *Focus – The Future of Your Company Depends On It* by Al Ries, New York: Harper Business, 1997.

E. Focus Needs an Enemy

1. Know who your competitor is.
    a. If you become too diversified, you can't keep up with what your competitor is doing.

F. A Focus Is the Future

1. By keeping a sharp focus, you are helping to create the future.

2. Assess what consulting services sell the most, then look ahead so that you will survive into the future.
    a. Respond proactively to trends in the marketplace, being careful not to *lose* focus, but to incorporate trends into your current focus so that it becomes even sharper and evolves with the times.

3. While you continue to focus on your vision, your focus cannot be rigid. You can't predict the future, so your focus must be adjustable.

G. A Focus Is Internal as Much as External

1. Where are you investing your time, money and resources? Are you spending 80% of your time to generate 20% of your revenue?
    a. Eliminate *all* underperforming units of your business.

2. The Pareto principle states that 80% of your business comes from 20% of your clients.
    a. Focus on the 20% of your clients that give you 80% of the business. Focus on what's essential to be more effective.
    b. This principle applies to every aspect of your business. In our office I question everything we do, every piece of paper generated.

3. Avoid distractions.
    a. What's the difference between getting distracted and purposefully taking TIME OFF? Time off should give you increased creativity.

H.   A Focus Is What the Client Needs

1.   Attorneys need to know who the Certified Legal Nurse Consultant^{CM} is.

2.   We need to ask honestly, *"What do attorneys really need?"*
  a.   They need autonomous CLNC® consultants who can help them create the future of litigation and resolution of lawsuits.
  b.   Isn't this the *real* future we should be creating?

      CREATING BETTER ATTORNEYS

      CREATING A BETTER INSURANCE INDUSTRY

      CREATING A BETTER LEGAL SYSTEM FOR ALL INVOLVED

I.   A Focus Is Personal

1.   When you look at your VISION and ultimately at your company, both are a reflection of you.

IV.   WHAT A FOCUS IS NOT

A.   A Focus Is Not a Specific Product or Service

1.   Instead, it's a Vision that stands the test of time, that is still alive when your competitor comes in and duplicates exactly how you perform your services and charges less for them.

2.   Strategies.
  a.   Get beyond your list of services.
  b.   Determine what your business is really *about*, referring to your unique selling position (as discussed earlier).

B.   A Focus Is Not an Umbrella

1.   Focus is not a "big idea" to cover every possible service you could provide.

31

2.	Strategy.
a.	Avoid being overly abstract in your vision – again, rely strongly on your USP when defining your focus.

## C.	A Focus Does Not Appeal to Everybody

1.	Focus is not about trying to capture an entire market.
a.	No one CLNC® consultant can appeal to everyone.
b.	You can become very successful just focusing on a small segment of the market.

2.	Strategy.
a.	If you worry about trying to please everyone, see a therapist.

## D.	A Focus Is Not Hard to Find

1.	Remember, a focus is simple.
a.	Don't make the process of finding a focus more complex than it needs to be.

2.	Strategy.
a.	To find a focus all you have to do is:
(1)	Think like a client.
(2)	Think outside your own point of view – this may not be easy!
(3)	Focus on what will benefit the client.
(4)	Develop your USP to separate you from other CLNC® consultants.
b.	This strategy will enable you to respond quickly and appropriately to changes in the marketplace.

## E.	A Focus Is Not Instantly Successful

1.	Whatever your focus, it takes passion, persistence, drive, hard work to make it happen.

2.	The reason most people are not successful is that they're not willing to pay their dues.
a.	The very successful Certified Legal Nurse Consultant^CM does what the *less* successful consultant is not willing to do.

3. Strategy.
    a. You've got to show up as a Certified Legal Nurse Consultant^{CM} and put out the effort to be a competent professional with no guarantee of the end result and no guarantee of what your future holds.
        (1) The only thing that's certain is this: If you do nothing, that's exactly what you'll achieve.

F. Focus Is Not Necessarily Balanced

1. There is no tidy formula for real balance.

2. Strategy.
    a. Success is demanding – you have to be on fire.
        (1) The price of doing what you love is time, energy, attention, persistence – and focus.

G. A Focus Is Not a Strategy

1. Strategies will and should change.
    a. Your focus should be stable.

H. A Focus Is Not Forever

1. One day your focus may be obsolete.
    a. You will have to respond flexibly and change it.
    b. However, a strong focus can last for decades, so don't be too quick to change a focus that is working.

V. PURPOSEFUL VISION PLANNING

A. Vision Statement

1. Your vision statement is your core business purpose, the destination you see for yourself.
    a. A vision statement is very global.

B. **Mission**

1. Your mission is why you exist, what you do, what you intend to accomplish.
   a. While vision is global, mission is more specific.
   b. Example – One component of Vickie Milazzo Institute's mission: *"We will master our destiny and inspire nurses to master theirs with passion, purpose and power. We are committed with enthusiasm to the belief that anything is possible."*

C. **Core Values**

1. Your core values are your basic business beliefs.

2. If you want to be a *great* company, honor and act on core values that embrace principles and high ideals.
   a. Example – At Vickie Milazzo Institute, clients are one of our core values. We exist because of our clients. We treat all clients professionally, respectfully and with integrity. We build superlative and life-long relationships with our clients.

D. **Objectives and Strategies**

1. Your objectives are your goals.
   a. You want to create:
      (1) Goals that are big, challenging and compelling.
      (2) Goals that are clear.
      (3) Goals that you can be committed to.
   b. As you reach each goal, you want to continue to set new goals that are as bold as the first goals you set for yourself.
      (1) Beware of the complacency that often accompanies success.

2. Strategies are the actions you implement to meet your objectives.
   a. Ask yourself, *"How do I get where I'm going?"*
   b. Implement your strategies.
      (1) Commit yourself to taking action today.
      (2) Act quickly.
      (3) Plan to make mistakes – accept the fact that some of your strategies will fail.
      (4) Take small steps every day.
      (5) Systemize effective strategies.

c. Strategy is important but remember, many successful companies have to experiment and fail in order to succeed.

E. Living with Your Vision and Mission

1. Reevaluate your vision and mission continually.
   a. Work with it, play with it and refine it.
   b. There is no final vision, mission, objectives and strategies – they are always evolving as you and your business evolve.

2. FOCUS – Your CLNC® practice depends on it!

Creating
Breakthrough
Systems

Vickie L. Milazzo, RN, MSN, JD

CREATING BREAKTHROUGH SYSTEMS

I. DEFINITION

    A. System

        1. Any formulated, regular or special method or plan for proceeding

II. WHY DO WE NEED SYSTEMS?

    A. Survival

        1. Systems are essential just to survive.

        2. Systems are essential to satisfy the market.
            a. Simple, logical systems are powerful tools for success.
            b. Ideally your systems should be designed to satisfy the few clients who are responsible for 80% of your revenues.

    B. Time-Efficient

        1. If an organized system is in place, you don't have to stop and think how to do something. Your action becomes automatic, a habit.
            a. Once implemented, an effective system will save both time and money.

    C. Consistency

        1. A system is independent of the person using it.

        2. Systems create consistency in the work product being generated.

D.   Quality

1.   Systems improve the quality of your work.

2.   You set the *standards* for your work through systems.

E.   Cost-Efficient

1.   Systems lead to a more cost-efficient operation.

F.   Evaluation Tool

1.   Systems are the foundation from which you evaluate everything and everyone.

G.   Open the Door for a Larger Vision

1.   Having systems in place allows you to:
         a.   Focus on the larger picture.
         b.   Take your practice to the next level.

2.   Every time some aspect of your business is systemized effectively, you are free to use the energy no longer needed for the routine task to create and innovate.

H.   Life-Enhancing

1.   You created your practice in order to have a life, not to give up your life.

2.   Larry Goodman (*Inc.*, Jan. 1998) states that, unlike a wage earner, you can ask and act on the answers to 4 basic questions:
         a.   What do I need and want out of life?
         b.   How can my company help me accomplish that?
         c.   What would such a company look like?
         d.   And how do I get it to look like that?

3.   Systemize the process of creating a life-enhancing business.

III. MODELS FOR SYSTEMS

A. McDonald's and Other Fast Food Chains

1. Large fast food chains, like McDonald's or Burger King, have many systems in place.
    a. They are all over the world; yet, no matter where you go, the french fries and hamburgers are the same.
    b. Teenagers staff the places; yet, what they say and what they do are the same.
    c. Systems are in place for every procedure:
        (1) How long to cook french fries.
        (2) How to clean the griddle.
        (3) How long to keep a sandwich on the warmer.
        (4) What to say to the customer.

2. The result is consistency and customer satisfaction.

B. Disneyland

1. Every aspect of the Disney operation reflects a dependence on and adherence to systems.
    a. Cleanliness of grounds.
    b. Service.
    c. Changing costumes out of sight of children.
    d. Friendliness.
    e. Dress and grooming.

2. The result is a friendly, consistent operation with few visible faults and a high degree of customer satisfaction.

C. Neiman-Marcus/Nordstrom's

1. Systems are in place for excelling in customer service.
    a. This keeps customers coming back for more.

D. Telemarketing Companies

1. They have systems for: what to say; how to say it; when to say it; how to close the deal and when to cut and run.

2. They rely heavily on scripts, role playing and scheduling for every activity in every part of the day.

IV. CREATING AND IMPLEMENTING EFFECTIVE SYSTEMS

A. Assessment

1. Identify aspects of your business that could benefit from systems:
   a. Routine procedures and routines that lend themselves to a system.
   b. Problems that could be corrected with the right system.

2. Make your assessment complete, systematic and continuous.
   a. Base your assessment on both subjective and objective data.

B. Diagnosis

1. Diagnose a comprehensive set of systems you intend to implement to handle the routine procedures or address the problems you identified in your assessment.

2. For each system be prepared to answer this question: "What are the ramifications of not having a system in place?"

C. Planning

1. Develop a plan of action for implementing the systems you have devised to help you meet your goals and objectives.

2. Develop strategies to implement your systems.

3. Apply the KISS principle.

4. Include the person who is most knowledgeable about each system in the planning process.

5.   Develop a written procedure for each system.

6.   Apply large corporate strategies and systems to your small business.

D.   Implementation

1.   Implement training and development programs for your systems.

2.   Implement the system.

3.   Adhere to the system consistently.

E.   Evaluation

1.   Once the system is in place, evaluate it for effectiveness.

2.   Refine the system based on your analysis of these evaluations.

3.   Revise written policies and procedures accordingly.

4.   Don't fear change.

5.   Miscellaneous tips.

F.   Ongoing Circular Process

1.   Creating and implementing systems is an ongoing process of assessing, diagnosing, planning, implementing and evaluating.

V.   WHAT NEEDS TO BE SYSTEMIZED? ANYTHING AND EVERYTHING

A.   Vision and Mission

1.   "You have to plan and visualize what you want for your business and *yourself* in the future. Because if you don't you don't own it."
               – Michael Gerber

B. Core Values

1. Successful Certified Legal Nurse Consultants^{CM} have and live by CORE VALUES.

C. Decision-Making

1. Effective CLNC® consultants make effective decisions using a decision-making system:
    a. Define the issue.
    b. Determine the result or outcome you want to achieve.
    c. Identify and discuss relevant background information necessary to brainstorm the issue.
    d. Identify what has been done so far to deal with the issue.
    e. Brainstorm the issue for solutions.
    f. Address the pros and cons of each solution, considering the consequences and risks involved.
    g. Make the decision.
    h. Let it sit a while.
    i. Evaluate the results of the decision.
    j. Avoid "focus group" or committee mentality.

D. Time Management

1. Manage time effectively.
    a. In other words, manage yourself effectively.
        (1) Control your attention and what you put your attention on.
        (2) Approach your business with single-mindedness.
    b. Being effective means you practice in a certain way.
        (1) "You have to practice being effective, and eventually being effective becomes a habit."

        – Peter Drucker

2. Plan your daily work schedule.
    a. Use a day planner.
    b. Use a tickler system for deadlines.
    c. Break up brain-drain, repetitive or monotonous work.
    d. Plan weekly, monthly, quarterly and annually.
    e. Review your vision at least weekly.

3.   Schedule uninterrupted blocks of time for important, but *not* urgent activities.

4.   Delegate everything that someone else can do.

5.   Eliminate unnecessary and non-productive tasks.
        a.   Ask, "What would happen if I or an employee or subcontractor did not do this activity?"
        b.   Assess where your time goes.
        c.   Focus on eliminating distractors:
                (1)   Mail.
                (2)   Financial matters.
                        (a)   Invoicing and billing.
                        (b)   Collecting.
                (3)   Operations.
                (4)   Marketing.
                (5)   Meaningless meetings.
                (6)   Too many networking encounters.
                (7)   Mentoring and training subcontractors.
                (8)   Personal distractors, if working at home.
                (9)   The Internet.

6.   Identify and eliminate time-wasters caused by lack of systems.

E.   Marketing

1.   Set up systems for marketing.

2.   Focus on one or two breakthrough marketing ideas.
        a.   Work these breakthrough ideas single-mindedly to their fullest potential before moving to the next idea.
        b.   Implement a system for applying the breakthrough idea.
                (1)   Perfect your system for breakthrough idea #1.
                (2)   Optimize all the avenues of sustainable profit which that one idea holds.
                (3)   Only when you're confident that breakthrough idea #1 is perfected and systemized do you move to breakthrough idea #2.
        c.   Layer one breakthrough idea on top of another and you become a marketing guerilla.

3. Networking. **(Exhibit A)**
   a. Schedule events for networking.
   b. Develop "scripts" for networking at various events.

4. Telephone marketing. **(Exhibit B)**
   a. Assess the best time to schedule telephone marketing, and do your phone marketing during these times.
   b. Develop a script for phone marketing.
   c. Keep records of your efforts and follow-up.

5. Direct mail.
   a. Define your target market.
   b. Develop your marketing materials.
   c. Send out your promotional package.
   d. Schedule follow-up calls.
   e. Implement follow-up calls.

6. Advertising. **(Exhibit C)**
   a. Determine your advertising budget.
   b. Develop an advertising plan.
   c. Develop advertisements.
   d. Test different advertisements.
   e. Set up your advertising files on a vendor-by-vendor basis.
   f. Set up a tickler system for advertising deadlines.
   g. Consider trading advertising or services for ad space.
   h. Track the effectiveness of your advertising.

7. Internet marketing.
   a. Your website.
      (1) Develop a systematic approach to keep customers coming back to your site using:
         (a) Information that changes weekly.
         (b) Resources site visitors can use.
         (c) Medical news.
         (d) Common questions (FAQs).
      (2) Consider implementing a password section that only attorney-clients can get into.
      (3) Develop a system for assessing the effectiveness of your website.
   b. Banner ads.
   c. Search engines.
   d. Email.

8.	Interviews.
	a.	Prepare a script.
	b.	Prepare for the interview.
	c.	Use a follow-up form for self-evaluation and follow-up.
	d.	Be sure to follow-up each interview with a thank you card or letter for the interest shown in your company.

9.	Common questions.
	a.	Develop standard responses to questions asked most often about legal nurse consulting and your business in particular.
	b.	Post your answers to these questions on your website.
	c.	Incorporate your answers into your promotional package.

10.	Company image.
	a.	Create a systematic promotional package.
	b.	Make all aspects of company image consistent.

11.	Contact management system.
	a.	Develop and use a contact management system.

12.	Ongoing communication with your mailing list.
	a.	Create and implement effective ways to stay in touch with the clients, prospective clients and others on your mailing list, such as:
		(1)	Information newsletter.
		(2)	Surveys.
		(3)	Promotional materials.

13.	Track the effectiveness of your marketing strategies.
	a.	Determine what's working – then systemize it and stick with it.

**F.	Office Operations**

1.	Filing. **(Exhibit D)**
	a.	Organize your files by color-coding or by placing them in alphabetical or chronological order.
	b.	Keep a filing log and file everything as the work and paper come in to minimize build-up and make setting up files easier.
		(1)	As a general rule, paper should only cross your hands once.
	c.	Set up *hot* files for high priority items.

2. Tickler system.
   a. Use a Pendaflex file folder set up by days of month or alphabetically.
   b. Take advantage of computer programs for setting up your tickler system.
   c. Clean your files every six months.

3. Sorting mail.
   a. Set up a system for sorting mail.
      (1) What goes to *hot* files?
      (2) What goes to the tickler system?
      (3) What goes to a file drawer?
      (4) What goes in the trash?
   b. Sorting mail should be a quick process once this system is in place.

4. Telephone communication.
   a. Is there a back-up system in place if your primary phone line fails?
   b. Set up systems for handling all telephone communications:
      (1) Daily time to check voice messages.
      (2) Specific time of day to return phone calls.
      (3) System for answering incoming calls.

5. Supplies and equipment.
   a. Supplies. **(Exhibit E)**
      (1) Use an ordering form to keep track of supplies needed and determine the minimum and maximum amount of each item to stock.
   b. Equipment.
      (1) Keep an updated inventory of equipment for tax purposes.
      (2) Maintain a file of product information and warranties.
   c. Maintenance.
      (1) Keep a list of telephone numbers for maintenance.
      (2) Evaluate maintenance agreements for copiers and other equipment for cost-effectiveness.
      (3) Train at least two staff members in routine maintenance or troubleshooting of most office equipment.
   d. Updates.
      (1) Update your office equipment regularly.

6. Financials.
    a. Invest in a software package, such as *QuickBooks*.
    b. Accounts payable.
        (1) Vendors.
        (2) Commonly recurring charges.
        (3) Payroll.
        (4) Quarterly tax returns.
    c. Accounts receivable and invoicing. **(Exhibit F)**
        (1) Set up a schedule for invoicing.
            (a) Use a tracking form for billable hours.
            (b) Set up a template for invoices on computer.
        (2) Systemize bank deposits.
        (3) Develop a system for collecting without emotional attachment.
    d. Tax records.
        (1) 1099s for subcontractors.
    e. Monthly financial statements and reconciliation of bank accounts.
    f. Key financial indicators.
        (1) Assess whether your systems are really making a difference.
        (2) Examples of key financial indicators to track:
            (a) Gross revenues.
            (b) Gross profit.
            (c) Number of cases per month.
            (d) Number of services provided per client.
            (e) Number of new attorney-clients per month.
            (f) Number of days to collect receivables.
            (g) Number of interviews with new prospects per month.

G. Product Development and Delivery

1. Systemize the formats you use for your work product. For example:
    a. Develop forms for frequently performed services, such as screening cases and developing medical record chronologies.
    b. Develop a system for organizing, tabbing and paginating medical records.
    c. Develop a checklist for discovery.

2. Systemize specific services you provide, such as:
   a. Library research.
      (1) Maintain an updated file of references you frequently use, including a file of articles on specific topics and SOC.
   b. Locating expert witnesses. **(Exhibit G)**
      (1) Set up a file of resumes and other information on each expert you work with.
   c. Liaison with witnesses and experts.
      (1) Develop an orientation checklist for preparing witnesses.

3. Product delivery.
   a. Systemize your method of meeting deadlines.
   b. Systemize your subcontracting projects. **(Exhibit H)**

H. Managing Subcontractors or Employees

1. Develop systems to make subcontractors and employees more effective at what they do now and to prepare them for what they will do in the future.
   a. Your goal is for each person who works for you to become an expert at what they do.
   b. Create a system for hiring subcontractors and employees.

2. Set up a policy and procedure manual.
   a. A policy and procedure manual is essential for maintaining consistency, efficiency and quality.

3. Orientation.
   a. Make one person responsible for providing general orientation for new employees or subcontractors.

4. Training.
   a. With a system for doing the work already in place, educating an employee or a subcontractor about their job is easy.
   b. Systems are especially important for tasks that are not done on a regular basis.
   c. Take nothing for granted.
   d. Develop a lifetime commitment to training and education for yourself, subcontractors and employees.

5. Quality control.
   a. Monitor the quality of your work continuously.
   b. Demand that others who work for you be expert at what they do.
   c. Base performance reviews on the quality control system you have in place.

VI. TIPS FOR CREATING EVEN BETTER SYSTEMS

A. Don't Reinvent the Wheel

1. Plug into what already exists.
   a. Keep forms or templates on computer.
   b. Develop or purchase forms and use them, taking advantage of the numerous software packages for creating customized forms such as:
      (1) Employee manuals.
      (2) Hiring and interviewing.
      (3) Financial.
      (4) Mailing list maintenance.
      (5) Personal information manager (PIM).
      (6) Word processing.
      (7) Spreadsheets.
   c. Check with associations of businesses similar to yours for forms you can use.
   d. You can find resources for business management and other needs at a wide variety of sites, including:
      (1) Small Business Administration – sba.gov
      (2) *Inc.* Magazine online – inc.com
      (3) Homeworks – free advice from home-based office experts Paul and Sarah Edwards – homeworks.com
      (4) Business@Home – marketing, technology, finance and legal issues – gohome.com
      (5) Home Office Association of America – types of businesses that are potentially home-based – hoaa.com
      (6) American Express Corporation Small Business Exchange – information and forms – americanexpress.com/smallbusiness
      (7) CourtTV Small Business Law Center – forms and documents – courttv.com/legalhelp/business
      (8) US Business Advisor – forms and links to FAQs – business.gov

B. **Tackle Problems Head-On**

    1.   Frequently if there is a problem, it is systems-related.

    2.   Try to think "outside the box."

C. **Put Everything in Writing**

    1.   Never rely on memory.

Exhibit A

Networking Contact Log

EVENT	DATE SCHEDULED	CONTACT PERSON	PHONE #	COMMENTS

Exhibit B

Telephone Marketing

NAME	PHONE #	ADDRESS	DATE MAILED	DATE FOR FOLLOW UP	FOLLOW UP (ACTUAL)	FURTHER ACTION NEEDED	COMMENTS

Exhibit C

Advertising Log

Advertising Log - Classified Advertisements

200___ Publication	Jan	Feb	March	April	May	June	July	Aug	Sept	Oct	Nov	Dec
monthly/bimonthly/weekly												
monthly/bimonthly/weekly												
monthly/bimonthly/weekly												
monthly/bimonthly/weekly												
monthly/bimonthly/weekly												

Advertising Log - Display Advertisements

200___ Publication	Jan	Feb	March	April	May	June	July	Aug	Sept	Oct	Nov	Dec
monthly/bimonthly/weekly												
monthly/bimonthly/weekly												
monthly/bimonthly/weekly												
monthly/bimonthly/weekly												

53

Exhibit D

Filing Log

I.   Lateral File (my office)

A.   Top Drawer

1.   Red files – Client records by file #
        001 – Drury vs. Martin
        002 – Smith vs. Jones
        003 – Davis vs. XYZ Hospital

B.   Bottom Drawer

1.   Blue Files – Standards (alphabetically)
        ANA
        AMA
        JCAHO
        Orthopedic

II.   Four-Drawer File

A.   Top Drawer

1.   Yellow files (expert resumes filed alphabetically by specialty)
        Anesthesia
                Melissa Smith, RN
        Cardiac
                David Nance, MD
                Patricia Miller, RN
                Joyce Sonoma, RN
        OB
                Susie Anchorage, RN
                Mary Moore, RN
                Richard Tent, MD

Exhibit E

Office Inventory

DESCRIPTION	STOCK	MAX	MIN	HAVE	ORDER
SUPPLY CABINET					
Globe Weis Accordion File Pockets, Expands to 5-1/4 inches. Legal (5 Pack)	449-785	6 Pks # 30	2 Pks # 10		
Envelopes Clasp	341-008	1 Bx	.5 Bx		
File Folders-Legal/3rd cut (#100 Bx)	301-838	2 Bx	1 Bx		
File Folders-Letter/3rd cut (#100 Bx)	316-471	2 Bx	1 Bx		
Globe Weiss Hanging Folders-Legal 1/5 cut (#25 Bx) Blue/Purple	315-036 449-991	2 Bx 2 Bx	1 Bx 1 Bx		
Imagination Diskettes (IBM Format) (# 10/Pk)	630-749	4 Bx	1.5 Bx		
Plastic Pages-Clear	432-666	1 Bx	½ Bx		
Plastic Pages-Satin	478-206	1 Bx	½ Bx		
3M Transparencies (#50 Bx)	555-839	2 Bx	1 Bx		
Laser Printer Film	405-522	1 Bx	½ Bx		
Report Covers-Slide Lock FS11-C-50P (#50 Bx)	320-580	2 Bx	1 Bx		
Staples-Stanley Bostich (3 Bx/Pk)	361-709	8 Bx	2 Bx		
Acco World Fasteners-2 piece-2 inch cap. 2-3/4" centers (#50 Bx)	825-489	4 Bx	2 Bx		
# 1 Paper Clips 100ct/Bx 10 Bx/Pk (smooth finish)	308-478	4 Pk 40 Bx	1 PK 10 Bx		
Corner Office Binder Clips (small) (#12/Pk)	808-857	4 Bx (# 48)	2 Bx (# 24)		
Corner Office Binder Clips (med)	808-865	2 Bx	1 Bx		
Corner Office Binder Clips (lg)	308-957	2 Bx	1 Bx		

DESCRIPTION		STOCK	MAX	MIN	HAVE	ORDER
Adams Message Pads (12 Pad/Pk)		391-193	2 Pk	½ Pk		
Post It Tape Flags	Red	452-367				
	Blue	452-375	2 Pk	1Pk		
	Yellow	452-409				
Highland Post Its (# 12 Pads/Pk)		542-761	6 Pk	2 Pk		
Small Post Its		419-853	2 Pk	1 Pk		
Liquid Paper	Pen & Ink	182-444	# 4	# 2		
	Just for Copies	182-378	# 4	# 2		
	Dryline Refill	435917	# 2	# 1		
	Dryline	435859				
Scotch Tape		508-176	# 6	# 2		
Letter Openers		442-608	#2	#1		
Misc Colored Labels						
Pencils #2 (12/Bx)		116-939	10 Bx	4 Bx		
Major Accent Yellow Highlighter (#12/ Bx)		203-125	2 Bx (# 24)	1 Bx (# 12)		
Sanford Sharpie Fine Pt Marker (12/Bx) (permanent)	Black	203-349	4 Bx	1 Bx		
	Red	203-356	2 Bx			
Name Tags (#100/Pk)		124-214	10 Pk	5 Pk		
Calculator Cartridges		848-564	#2	#1		
Vis-a-View Transpar. Marker (#12/Bx)		680959	2 Bx	1 Bx		
Ball Point Pens	Black	848-903	# 36	# 12		
	Red	848-911	# 36	# 12		
Push Pins			2 Bx	1 Bx		
Batteries	AA (8 Pk)	416545	# 24	# 12		
	AAA (4 Pk)	343-772	# 12	# 6		
	9 V (2 Pk)	343-731	# 6	# 3		
Misc Labels						
Adding Machine Paper (2-1/4"-12/Pk)		302-174	2 Pk	#8		

DESCRIPTION	STOCK	MAX	MIN	HAVE	ORDER
Legal Size Pads (#12/Pad)	305-342	#12	#4		
Colored Paper	628-941	1 Pk	½ Pk		
Colored Card Stock	645-473	1 Pk	½ Pk		
Union Camp Great White Laser Paper 20 Lb (10 Ream/Case) Legal Letter Hewlett Packard Letter	679-985 680-017 333-465	3 R 20 R	1 R 10 R		
Avery Reinforcements (#200/Pk)	113-167	1 Pk	½ Pk		
Wilson Jones Binder (3-ring Poly)	367-771	#2	#1		
Wilson Jones Binder (3-ring Poly)	367-797	#2	#1		
Fax Paper	374-280	#1	#1		
Certificate Paper	33-165	#4	#1		
FILE ROOM					
Xerox XC1045 #6R881	140-319	#2	#1		
Canon Cartridge A30	400-424	# 1	# 0		
Laser HP Cartridge 06A	371-609	# 1	# 0		
Laser HP Cartridge 98A	542-423	# 2	# 1		
HP 516 *29A* Inkjet Print Cartridge	239-301	#2	#1		
HP 51649A Inkjet Print Cartridge	239-319	#2	#1		
CONFERENCE ROOM					
Envelope Moistener Bottles	954-842	#6	#2		
Envelopes #10 Letter		3 Bx	1 Bx		
Envelopes (Lg Mailer)		3 Bx	1 Bx		
Envelopes (Survivor Tyvek-10x13 1st Class-Border/Self-seal-#50/Bx)	434-977	2 Bx	1 Bx		
Easel Paper Pads	106-328				

DESCRIPTION		STOCK	MAX	MIN	HAVE	ORDER
RECEPTION OFFICE						
Pyramid Time Cards		699-850	3 Pk	1 Pk		
Time Clock Ribbons			#3	#1		
Avery Labels	(5160)	364-364	4 Bx	2 Bx		
(Mailer)	(5161)	364-372	4 Bx	2 Bx		
(6/Sheet)	(5164)	463-646	2 Bx	1 Bx		
(Diskette)	(5196)	463-604	2 Bx	1 Bx		
INVOICING OFFICE						
Blank Envelopes		942-391	1 Bx	.5Bx		
Envelopes-#10 Letter (Window)			3 Bx	1 Bx		
Dot Matrix Ribbon		914-754 618-538	#3	#1		
Manila Expand File		422-170	#1	#5		
BACK OFFICE						
Letter-size Sheet Protectors		399-287	#2	#1		
Letter-Size Index Tabs		399-253	#2	#1		

Exhibit F

Billable Hours

Client Name: _____

File #: _____

DATE	TIME START	TIME END	TASK	TOTAL
4-2	8 a.m.	10 a.m.	Literature Search	2
4-2	10:30 a.m.	12:00 p.m.	Paginate Records	1.5
4-3	7:00 a.m.	12:00 p.m.	Review Records	5
4-5	9:30 a.m.	10:00 a.m.	Verbal Screening Report	.5
Month_____		**Total Billable Hours**		

Exhibit G

Expert Tracking Form

File # or Client Name	Type Needed	Potential Expert	Phone #	Date Contacted	Strengths	Weaknesses

Exhibit H

Subcontractor Form

Date Sent	Subcontractor	Tasks Assigned	Expected Due Date	Date Received

How to Build the Power Within

Vickie L. Milazzo, RN, MSN, JD

HOW TO BUILD THE POWER WITHIN

I.   INTRODUCTION

II.   PERSONAL POWER – YOUR LIFELONG JOURNEY

    A.   Personal Power Takes You to Success

        1.   To succeed on a high level you must possess a strong sense of self. You must trust yourself.

        2.   Frequently external factors validate your fears and create doubt.

        3.   Your mind is the vessel that holds your strength. Tend it, nurture it carefully.

    B.   Achieving Personal Power Is a Lifelong Journey

        1.   Learning to find and build on your strength is a lifelong journey.

        2.   You choose to be powerful or powerless.

        3.   If you choose to be powerful:
           a.   The rewards are great.
           b.   The challenges are many.

C.   **Assess Your Journey**

    1.   The journey takes you through many lessons.

    2.   Do a strength journey assessment.

III.   THE SOURCE OF YOUR PERSONAL POWER

A.   **The Source of Your Personal Power Is Within You**

    1.   No external factor or person brings or gives you your strength.

    2.   Your power is already there. Your greatness is within. All you have to do is reach in and grab hold of it.

    3.   To discover the source of your strength and to trust that it is already within you is in itself a journey, process or evolution.

B.   **Exercise Your Power Muscles**

    1.   Building your inner power is no different from building stronger and larger biceps muscles.

    2.   It takes concentration, focus and dedication.

    3.   Assess the power muscles you need to work on.

    4.   Because we're human, it's easy to get caught up in fear and low self-esteem.

Exercise: What current beliefs support your personal power?

What current beliefs disempower your inner strength?

What gives you your strength? What is the source of your personal power?

Exercise: Create an affirmation you will wake up to and go to bed with each night.

C.   Connect with Your Inner Power and Your Spirit Will Sing

IV.   USING YOUR INNER POWER TO MEET CAREER CHALLENGES

A.   Choosing a Career

B.   Choosing a Hospital Employer

C.   Choosing a Nursing Specialty

D.   Choosing to Start Your Own Company

E.   Career Crises or Disappointments

F.   Career Challenges and Adventures

G.   Integrating Success into My Life

Exercise: Identify a unique period in your career where you had to draw on your personal power.

Describe the situation.

Describe what you did to draw on your strength.

What unique skills did you apply to the particular situation?

V. BREAKTHROUGH STRATEGIES FOR BUILDING THE POWER WITHIN

A. **Set Yourself Up for Success**

1. Do small things that allow you to succeed.

2. What seems like a small step is really a giant leap.

3. Allow yourself to be creative.

4. Practice relying on your own power.

B. **Believe in Your Own Inner Strength**

1. Have faith in your journey.

2. If I fear there are obstacles in my way, then it's helpful to remind myself who creates the obstacles.

3. Avail yourself of your assets that give you the competence to build your personal power.

C. **Connect with Others Who Serve as Models and Who Will Support You in Your Journey**

1. Detach from anyone who does not support you.

D. **Take Care of Yourself, Nurture Yourself, Heal Yourself, Care for Yourself**

1. Health and physical image.

2.   Spiritual practice.

3.   Emotional.

4.   Mental.

5.   Social.

6.   Financial.

7.   Do for yourself what you need to do to spark your capacity to think BIG.

E.   Take Full Responsibility for Yourself

1.   Release all thoughts of blame and self-pity.

2.   Love and accept yourself.

3.   Carry your own monkey.

F.   Live Your Life with Integrity and Honor

G.   Empower Yourself with Knowledge and Study the Masters

H.   Control Your Thoughts

I.   **Live Every Single Day to the Fullest**

J.   **Set Goals in Every Area**

1.   Set realistic written goals you can achieve.
   a.   Example – I want to earn $20,000 from my part-time CLNC® practice this year, go full-time next year, and earn $100,000 within five years.
   b.   Be realistic.
   c.   Also have some big dreams.
   d.   State your goals in the present tense as though you're already accomplishing it.
   e.   Read your goals aloud daily.
   f.   Assess your progress nightly.

2.   Be sure your goals support each other.

3.   Be sure you have a plan to achieve your goals.

4.   Are you willing to do what it takes?
   a.   Pay your dues.
   b.   The path to personal power is demanding and rigorous.
   c.   Exercise discipline.

5.   Are you setting a goal you've already achieved?

6.   Develop a 25-year plan for yourself.

K.   **Repetition**

L.   **Conclusion**

Exercise: Set a goal for taking care of yourself, nurturing yourself, healing yourself, and caring for yourself in each of the following categories:

1.   Health and physical image.

2.   Spiritual practice.

3.   Emotional.

4.   Mental.

5.   Social.

6.   Financial.

VI.   CONCLUSION

A.   Make an Agreement with Yourself to Do Whatever You Need to Do to Build the Power Within

B.   We Are Called to Travel This Journey – Remember, "This Is the Moment" – Seize It

C.   May the Power Be with You

VII. REFERENCES

Blanchard, Kenneth, Oncken, William, Jr., and Burrows, Hal. *The One Minute Manager Meets the Monkey*. New York: Quill William Morrow, 1989.

Canfield, Jack, and Hansen, Mark Victor. *Dare to Win*. New York: Berkley Books, 1994.

Carlson, Richard. *Don't Sweat the Small Stuff*. New York: Hyperion, 1997.

Cohen, Alan. *The Dragon Doesn't Live Here Anymore*. New York: Ballantine Books, 1990.

Cohen, Alan. *I Had It All the Time*. Hawaii: Alan Cohen Publications, 1995.

Covey, Stephen R. *First Things First*. New York: Simon & Schuster, Inc., 1994.

Covey, Stephen R. *The 7 Habits of Highly Effective People*. New York: Simon & Schuster, Inc., 1989.

Csikszentmihalyi, Mihaly. *Creativity*. New York: HarperPerennial, 1997.

Dyer, Wayne W. *Manifest Your Destiny*. New York: HarperCollins Publishers, Inc., 1997.

Dyer, Wayne W. *Your Sacred Self*. New York: HarperCollins Publishers, 1995.

Fulghum, Robert. *Maybe (Maybe Not)*. New York: Villard Books, 1993.

Fulghum, Robert. *Uh-Oh*. New York: Villard Books, 1991.

Hill, Napoleon. *The Master-Key to Riches*. New York: Ballantine Books, 1965.

Hill, Napoleon. *Think and Grow Rich*. New York: Ballantine Books, 1988.

Hill, Napoleon. *You Can Work Your Own Miracles*. New York: Ballantine Books, 1971.

Hoff, Benjamin. *The Tao of Pooh*. New York: The Penguin Group, 1982.

Lee, Blaine. *The Power Principle*. New York: Simon & Schuster, 1997.

Morrissey, Mary Manin. *Building Your Field of Dreams*. New York: Bantam Books, 1996.

Peck, M. Scott. *Further Along the Road Less Traveled*. New York: Simon & Schuster, 1993.

Sartwell, Matthew, Editor. *Napoleon Hill's Keys to Success*. New York: The Penguin Group, 1994.

Spence, Gerry. *How to Argue and Win Every Time*. New York: St. Martin's Griffin, 1995.

Stone, W. Clement, and Hill, Napolean. *Success Through a Positive Mental Attitude*. New York: Pocket Books, 1987.

The Power of CLNC® Focus – Who Are We?

Vickie L. Milazzo, RN, MSN, JD

THE POWER OF CLNC® FOCUS –
Who Are We?

I.   LEADERS HAVE A FIRM UNDERSTANDING OF WHO THEY ARE

    A.   Leaders Know How to Focus

    B.   Leaders Know How to Ask the Right Questions to Find Their Focus

II.   FOCUSING ON THE ANSWERS TO RE-CREATE OURSELVES AS LEADERS AND PROFESSIONALS

    A.   Question # 1 – Who Are We?

    B.   Question # 2 – Who Do We Want to Be?

    C.   Question # 3 – Who's Deciding Who We Are?

    D.   Question # 4 – Can We Be Both Paralegals and Consultants?

    E.   Question # 5 – What Does the Legal Industry Really Need?

    F.   Question # 6 – What Do We Need to Do to Proactively Create the Future of Who We Are as Professionals?

        1.   Speak up loudly, voice your opinions.

        2.   Battle paralegal-based legal nurse consulting programs head-on.

        3.   Refuse to support associations and companies that are in bed with this enemy of nursing.

4. Support those who *support* you!

5. Write to the ABA.

6. Write to the AALNC.

7. Reject the role and title and second-class status of paralegal or legal assistant.

8. Let's insist on being treated like professional legal nurse consultants.

III. THE CHOICE IS YOURS – IF YOU GRAB IT!

A. The U.S. Is a Great Country!

B. What's Your Choice?

C. Join the Revolution!

D. Love What You Choose to Be!

E. Keep the Momentum Going

Speaker Biographies

SPEAKER BIOGRAPHIES

Evie Baron-Hernandez

Evie Baron-Hernandez has over 20 years of marketing, sales and customer service experience. She is a marketing creative and mentor for Vickie Milazzo Institute and has trained thousands of Certified Legal Nurse Consultant^{CM} entrepreneurs on how to plan and implement their marketing strategies. She has developed training programs in sales and marketing for the Institute, its staff and Certified Legal Nurse Consultants^{CM}. She is also part of the Institute's faculty and speaks at the *National Alliance of Certified Legal Nurse Consultants* Conference.

Vickie L. Milazzo, RN, MSN, JD

Founder and president of Vickie Milazzo Institute, Vickie single-handedly pioneered the field of legal nurse consulting in 1982. According to *The New York Times*, she "crossed nursing with the law and created a new profession." Her master's degree in nursing, with a concentration in education, and her law degree uniquely qualified Vickie to invent this profitable career opportunity for RNs.

The Institute is the oldest and largest legal nurse consulting training institute and the only publishing company exclusively devoted to this field. In 1994, Vickie developed the trademark CLNC® Certification Program, the first national legal nurse consulting certification. She then built the *National Alliance of Certified Legal Nurse Consultants (NACLNC®)*, a professional association of approximately 6,000 members. Nationally recognized by attorneys, the CLNC® Certification is the official certification of the *NACLNC®*.

Vickie has trained, coached and mentored more than 14,000 RNs as Certified Legal Nurse Consultants^{CM}, empowering them to take control of their lives, create exciting nursing careers and achieve financial freedom. She is recognized as the nation's expert on legal nurse consulting and as a dynamic role model by tens of thousands of nurses. Vickie teaches the innovative business strategies that changed the face of nursing and earned her a place on the national list of *Inc.* Top 10 Entrepreneurs.

Vickie is the editor of the bimonthly electronic newsletter *Legal Nurse Consulting Ezine*, available at LNCEzine.com. She is the author of the national bestsellers: *Core Curriculum for Legal Nurse Consulting®*; the CLNC® Certification Program; the Private and 2-Day *NACLNC®* Apprenticeships; *I Am a Successful CLNC® Success Journal*; *Create Your Own Magic for CLNC® Success*; and *Flash 55 Promotions: 55 FREE Ways to Promote Your CLNC® Business*.

She is also the author of the Amazon Top 10 business bestseller, *Inside Every Woman: Using the 10 Strengths You Didn't Know You Had to Get the Career and Life You Want Now*. Published by John Wiley & Sons, Inc., *Inside Every Woman* ranks in the top 10% of all business books sold nationwide. It is now in its fifth printing and is being published in five additional languages. Vickie delivers *Inside Every Woman* seminars across the country (seminar presentations are available on DVD and audio CD).

As the authoritative educator in her field, Vickie has been featured or profiled in numerous publications, including *The New York Times, St. Louis Post-Dispatch, Pittsburgh Business Times, L.A. Daily Journal, Houston Woman Magazine, NurseWeek, Entrepreneur, Small Business Success, Houston Chronicle, Texas Bar Journal, Cincinnati Enquirer, Ladies' Home Journal*™, various Gannett publications and in 220 newspapers reaching 16.6 million readers. Her work has been published everywhere from *USA Today* and *Seventeen* to *PINK* magazine and MSNBC.com, and in many nursing, legal and business publications, such as *Nursing Spectrum, Forensic Nurse, American Journal of Nursing, National Medical-Legal Reporter, Association of Trial Lawyers of America Newsletter, Lawyers Weekly USA* and *Entrepreneur's StartUps*.

A nationally acclaimed keynote speaker and member of the National Speakers Association, Vickie has spoken for groups such as the Association of Trial Lawyers of America, Texas Trial Lawyers Association, Farmers Insurance, Oncology Nursing Society and other business and professional organizations. She has educated thousands of nurses as an Internet chat host and has been interviewed on national radio and TV as an expert on legal nurse consulting, entrepreneurship and career advancement. Vickie's radio appearances have reached more than 20 million listeners. As a contributor to the NPR (National Public Radio) *All Things Considered* segment, *This I Believe*®, she shared her essay, *Stepping Out of Fear*. NPR has an audience of more than 26 million listeners.

Vickie's many honors include:

- *Inc.* Top 10 Entrepreneur – one of the top entrepreneurs in the U.S.
- Stevie Award for Women Entrepreneurs – Mentor of the Year
- *NurseWeek* Nursing Excellence Award for Advancing the Profession
- Most Innovative Small Business – Pitney Bowes
- Top 100 Small Businesses in Houston – *Houston Business Journal*
- Top 25 Woman-Owned Businesses in Houston, Top 50 Fastest Growing Woman-Owned Businesses and Top 10 Woman-Owned Businesses Ranked by Largest Percentage of Revenue Growth – *Houston Business Journal*

Vickie earned her bachelor of science in nursing at the University of St. Thomas and her master of science in nursing at Texas Woman's University, both in Houston. She earned her juris doctor at South Texas College of Law.

In all her work Vickie openly shares her practical and proven strategies as she coaches and mentors nurses to take charge of their professional destiny. Vickie is a powerful advocate for women in business and for nurses. Her vision is to revolutionize nursing careers one RN at a time. Her audiences are transformed and inspired to action by her extensive business expertise, irresistible drive and vibrant energy. The most common refrain from CLNC® consultants attending her seminars is, *"She changed my life!"*

Tamara Schilling, RN, BSN, CLNC

Tamara Schilling, founder of Med Evidence, a successful CLNC® firm in San Francisco, was a legal nurse consultant for seven years. She now resides in Denver, and is a full-time writer and motivational speaker. Tamara continues to be actively involved in legal nurse consulting as a CLNC® Mentor for Vickie Milazzo Institute. In this role she continues her passion to inspire and assist other nurses in their CLNC® practices, helping them build their businesses, overcome challenges and reach their dreams. Her mission is to see you succeed.